MY FIRST CHESS CLUB

By David Cohen

&

Sofia Polgar

ACKNOWLEDGEMENTS

David thanks his wife, Lisette Lu, and his parents, Edward & Irma Cohen.

Sofia thanks Mom and Dad, Klara & Laszlo, for bringing her up to become the person she is and her sisters Judit and Susan, who are also her best friends.

DEDICATION

Dedicated to Ted & Heidi Winick

Text written and copyright © 2020 by David Cohen

Rhymes written and copyright © 2020 by Sofia Polgar
Illustrations drawn and copyright © 2020 by Sofia Polgar
Book design: Sofia Polgar

Author photograph by Carlos Esteves copyright © 2011 by David Cohen
Illustrator photograph by Timea Jaksa
Photos used by permission of Judit Polgar Chess Foundation
Additional photography by Carlos Esteves copyright © 2011 by David Cohen

Published by David Cohen, Toronto, Ontario, Canada

Book (softcover): ISBN 978-0-9809214-5-8
Electronic book: ISBN 978-0-9809214-6-5

MY FIRST CHESS CLUB

SMILE!

Every Tuesday morning at 8:00, I go to my school one hour before my classes start.

I join my friends in the library for Chess Club.

I have an extra hour or so
To the library I go

My friends are already waiting
On checkered boards they're playing

Our teacher doesn't know much about chess. But teacher knows a lot about children!

Sometimes I have an argument with the friend I am playing chess with. We argue about our game. Maybe a piece was put on the wrong square. Maybe we're not sure about the rules.

We get mad at each other. Teacher comes over and makes us stop arguing. "Smile!", teacher says.

Teacher waits until we are both smiling. I can't be mad when I'm smiling. Teacher goes away only when we are no longer mad at each other.

Then the other kid and I talk things over. We figure out what went wrong. Then we get back to playing.

After the game, we both go away happy. We are friends.

Look at the knight - this jumpy creature
Smile! Demands our friendly teacher

F O C U S !

Sometimes my mom stays to talk with our teacher.

She tells teacher: "In her entire life until now, I've never seen her sit still!"

Knights jump and bishops are running
I sit and find this all very interesting

It's true! At home, I'm always running around, driving my mom crazy.

But, at Chess Club, I sit still in my chair.

I concentrate on one thing: my chess game.

I watch where my friend moves the chess piece.

I think about my move. Then I make up my mind and I play my move.

When I am still and focus all my attention on the game, then I play well.

Check out the rook balance!
Hope this tower will not dance...

FIRST THINK,
THEN MOVE!

After I move my chess piece, I let go. Then I can't take it back.

I have to accept the choice I made.

To avoid mistakes, I take time to think carefully about my move, before I make it on the chessboard!

I love drinking chocolate milk
Before my move I better think

It's the same in life, with my friends.

When I say something, I can't take it back. Someone already heard me.

When I do something, I can't take it back. Someone already saw me.

I have to accept what I said or did.

To avoid mistakes, I take time to think carefully about what I say and do, before I say and do it!

I listen to the teacher's voice
Then try to make a better choice

SHARE
WHAT YOU KNOW!

Each year, our school enters a team of four players in a chess tournament where we compete against other schools. We always win our game on Board One, because we have the best player in the city on our team! However, we lose all the rest of our games. We have fun meeting other kids and playing, but we aren't so good at competing.

Our team goes to a big tourney
Lots of fun during this journey

Sometimes I lose three games in a loop
It's still fun to be with my favourite group

This year, our teacher asked our best player to teach us to play better!

She always wins. No fun for us! Boring for her!

Now, she watches us play. When we make a mistake, she tells us to take it back. Then, she asks us if we could have made a better move. We think about the choices. If we can't find a better move, then she shows us the move that she would make. She explains why it's a better move.

In practice games, we help each other make better moves.

We are a real team!

Our friend has lots of tricks to show
She teaches moves that we will know

Winning a championship is a dream
Until then I love my team

CLEAN UP
AFTER YOURSELF!

At the end of a chess game, we always put the chess pieces back in their starting positions on the chessboard. We can tell right away if a piece is missing. Then the chess set is ready for the next game.

At the end of Chess Club, we do this one more time. We know that we are putting away a complete chess set, ready for the next Chess Club.

Next, we put the tables and chairs back in their usual places. Everything is ready for the kids at school to use the library.

Knight, rook, bishop go back in the box
Green trees save lives of elephant and fox

It's the same in life, with my family. When I'm done with my books and toys, I put them away, so I won't trip on them. I like to help keep our home clean, so it's more pleasant to live in.

When I play in the park, I pick up my stuff before I leave. I want to keep our environment clean.

The chess queen and king have their base
Let's keep this world a lovely place!

TIME TO PLAY!

Girls and boys it's time to play
Where is the chess board anyway?

ABOUT THE AUTHORS

Author

David Cohen is a Toronto, Canada chess club organizer, tournament director, teacher, writer and editor.
He earned his Bachelor's degree in Commerce (Accounting) at the University of Ottawa and his Master's degree in Management at Yale University.

With Ted Winick, he co-founded Chess Institute of Canada to teach Ted's life lessons through chess.

Illustrator

Sofia Polgar is a Hungarian born chess champion, artist and illustrator. She was 1986 World Girls Under-14 Chess Champion. At the Women's Chess Olympiads, she won 2 team and 3 individual gold medals.
She is co-author and artist for the award winning Judit Polgar Chess Palace educational program. She met her husband Yona Kosashvili through chess and they live in Israel with their two sons, Alon and Yoav.

PLAY WITH FRIENDS!

When we play and the game ends
Win or lose we are still friends!

RECOMMENDED READING

If you would like to learn how to play chess, then you can read these books with a parent or teacher:

1.   Comprehensive Chess Course, Volume 1 by Roman Pelts, 1986.

2.   Chess is Child's Play by Laura Sherman and Bill Kilpatrick, 2012.

If you would like to learn more, then you can read these books:

Alexey Root has written many books which are both educational and fun. They can help you learn chess together with math, science, reading, writing and social studies:

3.   Science, Math, Checkmate: 32 Chess Activities for Inquiry and Problem Solving, 2008

4.   Read, Write, Checkmate: Enrich Literacy with Chess Activities, 2009

5.   People, Places, Checkmates: Teaching Social Studies with Chess, 2010

Sofia's sisters Susan Polgar and Judit Polgar have written many books to help you play chess better.

For Parents

More about life lessons which you can learn through chess:

1.   Why teach chess in schools? by Uvencio Blanco, 1998.

2.   Teaching Life Skills Through Chess: A Guide for Educators and Counselors by Fernando Moreno, 2002.

PLAY ON ANY BOARD OR ONLINE!

Pretty pieces on the board
You will never again be bored!

REVIEWS

"The best chess book ever drawn!"
- Arthur Kogan,
Chess Grandmaster

"Chess develops countless life skills.
This book is a great illustration of it!"
- Susan Polgar,
Women's World Chess Champion

"I loved playing chess at my school chess club and this book made me remember why!"
- Matthew Sadler,
Chess Grandmaster

"My First Chess Club shows how playing chess, under the supervision of a caring teacher, conveys life lessons. At a school library chess club, children cooperate, focus attention, think before they move, and clean up when games are done. Author David Cohen distills his experience as a chess club organizer into useful lessons, while International Master Sofia Polgar's gifts in chess and artistic expression shine in her exquisite chess poems and illustrations."
- Dr. Alexey Root, Woman International Master,
author of Children and Chess: A Guide for Educators

CHESS CONNECTS US!

Little pawn and giant knight
Play with pieces black or white!

ABOUT TED AND THE BOOK

"I thoroughly enjoyed reading this book. The illustrations and the photos captured the essence of chess which is designed to bring people of all ages from all walks of life together. They also created the impression of just how many paths open up to those who engage in the game both locally and globally.

The story itself highlights the importance of all the life lessons taught through the medium of chess. It reiterates the importance of always considering the consequences of one's actions and taking responsibility for what we did. I love the parallels drawn between aspects of life and the game such as keeping our planet, homes and immediate environments clean and organized.

 Ted's words ring throughout the story - I was very fortunate to share the stage with him for decades as he reinforced the messages and echoed the sentiments expressed throughout the story. I was delighted to see a very accurate depiction of school chess team tournaments and the importance of unity and the critical role played by each and every player. Having organized team tournaments for decades and having played for many teams throughout my life, this has brought back fond memories. This segment of the story also highlights the critical element of the need to improve, the need to share information and the importance of goal setting- all critical pieces for children.

The joy of chess is clearly highlighted throughout the story. The game and all that it brings to life brings much joy to so many children who otherwise may not have an outlet where they can showcase their talents or shine. This is the essence of the story and will be understood by every educator who reads it and looks at the captions. There is a myriad of lessons embedded, sort of like the many variations in any given chess position on the board."

- Peter Boross-Harmer, School Principal & Founding Director, Chess Institute of Canada

Made in the USA
Monee, IL
16 January 2021